JOHN WAGNER
Writer

MICK McMAHON ★ RON SMITH
DAVID GIBBONS ★ BRIAN BOLLAND
BRENDAN McCARTHY ★ BRETT EWINS
GARRY LEACH
Artists

TOM FRAME ★ JOHN ALDRICH ★ JACK POTTER
PETER KNIGHT ★ TOM KNIGHT ★ DAVE GIBBONS
Letterers

MICK MCMAHON
Cover Artist

Creative Director and CEO: Jason Kingsley
Chief Technical Officer: Chris Kingsley
2000 AD Editor in Chief: Matt Smith
Graphic Novels Editor: Keith Richardson
Graphic Design: Simon Parr
PR: Michael Molcher
Reprographics: Kathryn Symes
Original Commissioning Editors:
Kelvin Gosnell and Steve MacManus

Published by Rebellion, Riverside House, Osney Mead, Oxford, OX2 0ES, UK.
www.rebellion.co.uk

ISBN: 978-1-78108-009-2
Printed by CPI Antony Rowe
First published: May 2013
10 9 8 7 6 5 4 3 2

Printed on FSC Accredited Paper

A CIP catalogue record for this book is available from the British Library.

For information on other 2000 AD graphic novels, or if you have any comments on this book, please email books@2000ADonline.com

To find out more about 2000 AD, visit www.2000ADonline.com

3

I DON'T... UNDERSTAND IT ...I DON'T **REMEMBER** GOING TO THE MEGA-TIMES OFFICE. I DON'T **REMEMBER** PULLING THAT TRIGGER ... YET SO MANY WITNESSES **SWEAR** THAT I DID THE KILLING... ... AM-- AM I GOING **MAD**?

OH BOY! JUST WAIT TILL THOSE TITAN DOCTORS GET THEIR MITTS ON YOU, DREDD!

YOU DON'T HAVE TO TELL **ME**, JACKASS! MY OWN **BROTHER** WAS ON TITAN! I KNOW WHAT THEY DO TO PEOPLE...

RICO...RICO... THAT I SHOULD END UP LIKE YOU--FOR A CRIME I DON'T EVEN REMEMBER COMMITTING...

DROKK IT! A CRIME I **DIDN'T** COMMIT!

I DIDN'T DO IT! IT'S A **FRAME UP**!

HA, HA! SAVE YOUR MUSCLES, PALLY! YOU'LL NEVER BREAK THOSE CHAINS!

YAAAAH!

UH?

MAYBE AT THAT MOMENT, DREDD **WAS** CRAZY! FOR ONLY THE SUPERHUMAN STRENGTH OF MADNESS COULD HAVE SNAPPED THAT CHAIN--

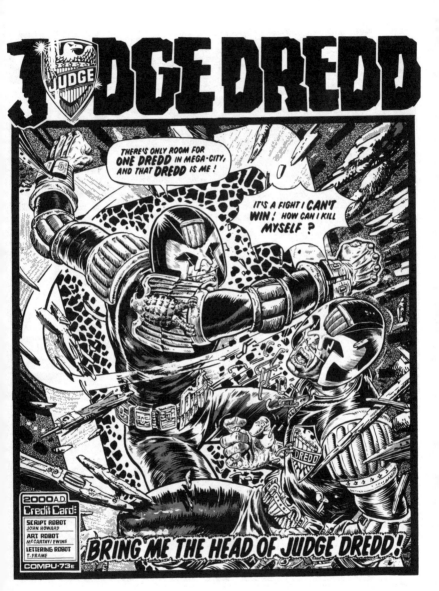

SENTENCED TO *TWENTY* YEARS ON TITAN FOR *MURDER*, JUDGE DREDD HAS ESCAPED— AND SPARKED OFF *THE BIGGEST MANHUNT IN MEGA-CITY HISTORY* . . .

YOU MEN HAVE YOUR IDENTIFICATION READY!

EVERYBODY OUT! WE'RE SEARCHING EVERY BUILDING IN THE CITY!

MEGA-CITY WON'T BE SAFE FOR AN HONEST CRIMINAL TILL THEY FIND JUDGE DREDD!

AT JUSTICE CENTRAL, WHERE DEPUTY CHIEF *JUDGE CAL* WAS ORGANISING THE MANHUNT . . .

I'M GOING TO MY QUARTERS TO REST, JUDGE CAL. LET ME . . . LET ME KNOW IF THERE'S ANY NEWS ON DREDD.

YES, YES! THE *CHIEF'S CHAIR* SUITS ME SO WELL! WHEN I HAVE DREDD'S HEAD I CAN MAKE THIS CHAIR *MY OWN!*

DREDD'S ARREST HAS HIT THE *CHIEF JUDGE* HARD, JUST LIKE I KNEW IT WOULD! HE'S OLD AND WEAK— TOO WEAK TO BE CHIEF JUDGE MUCH LONGER.

MEANWHILE IN A DARK CITY UNDERPASS . . .

♪ I GOT THE *PIN-STRIPE BLUES,* FROM MY HEAD TO MY SHOES, NO MAKE-UP NO BEARD-OH, I SURE AM A *WEIRDO!* ♪♪

WANT DRED

MAX, BABY, YOUR VOICE SOUNDS SWEETER THAN A BAND OF *ANGELS!* YEAH, SHAKE IT, MAX!

ERK!

JUDGE DREDD! HEY, BABY, EVERY MAN ON THE FORCE IS AFTER YOUR HEAD . . . AND IT AIN'T TO GIVE YOU A *HAIRCUT!*

THAT'S WHY I NEED YOUR *HELP,* MAX.

MAX NORMAL, THE PIN-STRIPE FREAK, WAS DREDD'S BEST INFORMER. THE JUDGE QUICKLY EXPLAINED HIS SITUATION TO HIM . . .

I DIDN'T DO THE KILLING, YET EYE-WITNESSES SWEAR IT WAS ME. SOMEBODY FRAMED ME, MAX — FRAMED ME BY USING A ROBOT!

A ROBOT THAT LOOKS AND ACTS JUST LIKE YOU...PHEW! THAT WOULD TAKE SOME MAKING. LEMME TICK IT OVER UPSTAIRS, BABY...

YEAAHH...THERE IS ONE DUDE. CHICK PARKER, AN ENGINEER OVER AT MODERNA ROBOTS. HE WAS RUNNING UP A LOT OF BAD DEBTS ON THE TABLES — THEN LAST WEEK HE SUDDENLY PAID THEM OFF.

YOU'RE A MARVEL, MAX! THANKS A MILLION!

NO-ONE NOTICED THE DARK FIGURE SCALING THE WALL OF MODERNA ROBOTS AN HOUR LATER —

LIGHT'S ON. HE'S WORKING LATE.

I WANT A TALK ABOUT A ROBOT YOU BUILT — AND I'M IN NO MOOD FOR LIES!

PARKER WAS IN NO MOOD FOR ANYTHING!

HE'S BEEN MURDERED! SHOT DEAD! BUT HOW . . .

I DID, DREDD. OR RATHER, YOU DID.

31

42

47

BUT A CITY DOES NOT DIE SO EASY. FOR EVERY ONE OF CAL'S JUDGES THERE WERE A *THOUSAND* ARMED MEN —

JUDGE DREDD WILL LEAD US TO VICTORY!

YOU'RE SENTENCED TO— *AAAGHH!*

MORE MEN! I MUST HAVE MORE MEN IN SECTOR 36!

ON A FLYOVER ABOVE THE BATTLE —

MAN OH MAN! I NEVER SAW ANYTHING LIKE THIS — NOT EVEN DURING THE ROBOT WARS!

TOO MANY GOOD PEOPLE ARE DYING, GIANT. WE'VE GOT TO ARM THEM PROPERLY...

MOUNT UP FOR THE ARMOURY DEPARTMENT!

THE SMALL CONVOY RACED THROUGH THE CITY STREETS, UNTIL —

HALT!

JUSTICE DEPT. ARMOURY EAST. D.

UH-UH, BABY—

WE'RE THROUGH!

WE'RE COMIN' THROUGH!

AAAGH!

49

THE INSANE JUDGE CAL HAS BECOME THE NEW CHIEF JUDGE OF MEGA-CITY ONE, BUT A FEW LOYAL JUDGES UNDER JUDGE DREDD HAVE INCITED THE PEOPLE TO REBELLION. NOW, AFTER TWO DAYS OF FIERCE FIGHTING, MUCH OF THE CITY LIES IN RUINS —

IN THE SPEARHEAD OF THE REBEL ATTACK WAS JUDGE DREDD...

CAL'S SENT REINFORCEMENTS! TAKE 'EM!

JUDGE DREDD!

AAAH!

WITH DREDD WERE TUTORS FROM THE ACADEMY OF LAW, CHOSEN FROM JUDGES WOUNDED IN ACTION...

SHOOT TO WOUND, MEN!

YOU'RE DEAD MEAT, JUDGE PEPPER!

WHY, IT'S JENKINS — CLASS OF '97...

UUGH!

YOU NEED SOME REFRESHER COURSES, BOY!

AAAAGH!

CAL'S MEN WERE SOON OVERPOWERED...

LOCK UP THOSE TRAITORS, BABY!

THOSE JUDGES WERE ALL MY PUPILS ONCE, DREDD. WHY DID THEY GO BAD?

ONLY CAL COULD ANSWER THAT, JUDGE GRIFFIN. THAT MADMAN'S GOT A LOT TO ANSWER FOR.

DREDD'S MEN ROARED INTO THE BATTLE ON THE CAPTURED BIKES...

INDIVIDUAL ACTION! HELP WHERE YOU'RE NEEDED!

AND SO MEGA-CITY'S BLACKEST HOURS ROLLED ON...

MIND YOU, AT THIS RATE THE EXECUTIONS COULD TAKE *YEARS*. I'LL GET JUDGE SLOCUM TO SPEED THINGS UP WHEN HE ARRIVES!

A MAJESTIC SIGHT, JUDGE COX. THE WORLD HAS KNOWN MANY TYRANTS, BUT *I* AM THE GREATEST OF THEM ALL. A TRUE TYRANT. A *TYRANT'S TYRANT!*

AT THAT MOMENT, NEARBY—

LOOK OUT!

CRAZY DRIVERS!

GET IN, SLOCUM!

WHAT THE—

MOVE IT, BOY!

DREDD! I SUPPOSE YOU'RE GOING TO KILL ME!

WRONG, SLOCUM. I'M GOING TO LET YOU LIVE— *BECAUSE YOU'RE GOING TO GET CAL TO STOP THE EXECUTIONS!*

Y-YOU'RE CRAZY! HOW CAN I MAKE CAL DO ANYTHING?

I'LL TELL YOU WHAT TO DO — *YOU JUST DO IT!*

BY EARLY AFTERNOON...

LOOKS LIKE THE EXODUS IS OVER, CHIEF JUDGE.

I WANT A *WALL* AROUND THE CITY — A WALL A *MILE HIGH* WITH SEARCHLIGHTS AND GUN EMPLACEMENTS! I WANT IT IN *THREE WEEKS!*

EXCELLENT! EXCELLENT! BUT WE MUST ENSURE THIS NEVER HAPPENS AGAIN...

TH-THREE WEEKS! B-BUT, CHIEF JUDGE, WHERE WILL WE GET THE WORKFORCE?

YOU HAVE A *WORKFORCE OF MILLIONS,* SLOCUM! YOU HAVE A *WHOLE CITY!*

THE WORK BEGAN. PRISONS WERE EMPTIED, EVERY ROBOT IN THE CITY WAS DRAFTED INTO SWELL THEIR NUMBERS, AND WHEN THE WORKFORCE DWINDLED, FRESH ARRESTS WERE MADE —

— WITH *TERRIFYING SPEED,* A *CONCRETE CURTAIN* WAS TAKING SHAPE AROUND MEGA-CITY ONE!

THE WORK WENT ON DAY AND NIGHT. BUT IT DID NOT GO UNOPPOSED —

THIS IS THE SECTION WE HIT TONIGHT, JUDGE DREDD.

REMEMBER, MEN, WE'RE FIGHTING A *GUERILLA* WAR NOW. HIT HARD, HIT FAST — AND THEN *GET OUT!*

JUDGE DREDD HAD VOWED TO SMASH CAL'S REIGN OF TERROR. WITH HIM WERE TUTOR JUDGES FROM THE CITY'S ACADEMY OF LAW —

ON THE OTHER SIDE —

DREDD GET ON BIKE HERE. HOUNDS LOSE TASTE, BUT SOON FIND AGAIN.

THEY FOLLOW BY TASTE OF TYRE RUBBER NOW.

THE STRANGE CONVOY RACED THROUGH THE CITY —

HIDE! THE HOUNDS OF HELL ARE COMING!

JUDGE DREDD'S BASE WAS A DISUSED UNDERGROUND GARAGE. WITH HIM WAS A HANDFUL OF LOYAL JUDGES, MOST OF THEM WOUNDED. TUTORS FROM THE ACADEMY OF LAW, AND THEIR NUMBERS WERE DWINDLING WITH EVERY RAID —

SORRY I... LET THAT KLEGG G-GET ME, JUDGE DREDD... I KNOW YOU CAN'T... CAN'T SPARE... ANY MEN...

YOU DID YOUR BEST, JUDGE PEACE. I WILL REMEMBER YOU WELL.

HE'S DEAD.

DROKK IT! IT WAS HARD ENOUGH FIGHTING OUR FELLOW JUDGES, BUT WITH THOSE ALIEN MERCENARIES ON THEIR SIDE... IT'S HOPELESS!

WHAT CAN WE DO, JUDGE DREDD? OUR LESSONS AT THE ACADEMY DON'T COVER HOPELESS SITUATIONS.

AARROOOOOO!

HOW CLEVER!! I REALLY MUST MAKE THEM JUDGES.

AARROOOO!

CAL IS THE CANCER AT THE HEART OF THE CITY. OUR DUTY IS CLEAR. WE MUST KILL HIM!

IT WILL BE A SUICIDE MISSION, BUT ONE OF US MAY GET THROUGH. IF CAL CAN BE DESTROYED, PERHAPS THE CITY WILL RETURN TO SANITY.

YES, THE RIGHT DECISION AS ALWAYS, JUDGE DREDD. THANK GOODNESS WE HAVE A LEADER LIKE YOU.

I TAKE SOME OF THE CREDIT FOR THAT, BY DOR! I TAUGHT HIM HIS "ADVANCED LEADERSHIP".

YOU TAUGHT CAL TOO, JUDGE PEPPER!

WELL?

THE MADMAN WANTS US TO *APPLAUD* THAT RUBBISH... SO *CLAP!* HE'S CRAZY ENOUGH TO HAVE US *ALL* KILLED!

BRAVO! YEEH-HA! 'RAA! WOWEE! Y

F-FORGIVE US, CHIEF JUDGE, FOR A MOMENT WE WERE, UH... *STUNNED* BY THE *BRILLIANCE* OF YOUR *WIT!*

JUDGES, TODAY IS THE THIRD HAPPIEST DAY OF MY LIFE. TODAY I HAVE MET MY GREATEST ENEMY... AND *SLAIN* HIM!

LET THERE BE *CELEBRATIONS* THE LIKE OF WHICH THIS CITY HAS NEVER SEEN! LET *EVERY CITIZEN* SHARE IN THE GREATNESS AND GLORY OF *CAL!*

SOON, ON CITYWIDE TELEVISION –

MCTV

NO LAWS

...AND AS A TOKEN OF HIS *SPECIAL FAVOUR,* CHIEF JUDGE CAL HAS DECREED THAT THERE WILL BE *NO LAW* FOR THE NEXT *24 HOURS!* CITIZENS ARE FREE TO DO AS THEY WISH, WITH *NO FEAR OF ARREST.*

WOW! IT-IT'S HARD TO BELIEVE! ONLY A *RAVING LUNATIC* WOULD MAKE *CRIME LEGAL!*

YEAH, CRAZY! IT'LL BE A *FREE-FOR-ALL* OUT THERE!

TWENTY SECONDS AFTER IMPACT, THE AIR-BAGS DEFLATED...

I...I'M ALIVE! ANY-ANYBODY ELSE?

GIANT HERE, JUDGE DREDD!

DREDD SWITCHED ON THE LIGHTS—

GRIFFIN, PEPPER AND KELSO SEEM OKAY—BUT I DON'T LIKE THE LOOK OF SCHMALTZ.

WHERE—WHERE THE HECK ARE WE? SEEMS LIKE WE WENT *THROUGH* CITY BOTTOM—AND OUT THE OTHER SIDE!

KINDA DARK OUT THERE. MAYBE WE'RE IN *HELL*, J.D. IT SURE *SMELLS* LIKE IT!

THE SMELL—OF COURSE! THIS IS THE OLD *OHIO RIVER*...THEY CALLED IT *THE BIG SMELLY*. IT GOT SO FOUL AND POLLUTED THEY HAD TO CONCRETE IT OVER.

DROKK IT, DOOR'S JAMMED! IT'LL HAVE TO BE OPENED FROM OUTSIDE.

THEN WE'VE GOT A LONG WAIT, BABY. AIN'T MANY FOLKS TAKE THEIR SUNDAY STROLL ALONG THE BIG SMELLY!

UHHH!

AN *UPSIDER* WRECK! RICH PICKIN'S MAYBE!

FOOD, CLOTHES, LOTSA THINGS!

BUT UP AHEAD, MANY TORCHES WERE FLICKERING ON THE BANKS OF THE FILTHY RIVER...

WE KILL THE *UPSIDERS* AN' TAKE *EVERYTHING*!

THERE ARE LIGHTS OUT THERE, J.D. COULD BE PEOPLE—*HEY!* THAT LOOKS LIKE A *GRAPPLING HOOK!*

AS CAL'S ALIEN MERCENARIES DRAGGED THE UNFORTUNATE ACTORS AWAY . . .

ANOTHER MAN WAS BROUGHT IN . . .

CONRED CONN, THE GREAT VID-PIC STAR!

THEY SAY HE'S THE HANDSOMEST MAN IN THE WORLD!

BUT HE RETIRED FROM SHOW BIZ. HE WANTED TO BE ALONE.

CITIZEN CONN, IT WILL BE YOUR PRIVILEGE TO PLAY THE GREATEST PART EVER WRITTEN— THE PART OF *ME!*

YOU KNOW I DON'T MAKE PICTURES ANY MORE, CHIEF JUDGE.

MIDGET, YOU HAVE BEEN CHOSEN TO PLAY THE PART OF *JUDGE DREDD* IN A *TV SPECTACULAR* I AM MAKING. IT WILL SHOW THE TRUE STORY OF MY *FEARLESS STRUGGLE* TO RESTORE LAW AND ORDER TO THIS CITY!

D-DON'T KILL ME, CHIEF JUDGE! I-I'LL DO IT!

I KNEW YOU'D COME ROUND. SPEND A FEW MINUTES ON YOUR KNEES AND WE'LL FORGET THIS LITTLE TIFF EVER HAPPENED.

FILMING WILL START IMMEDIATELY. WHEN THE PEOPLE SEE WHAT A GREAT HERO I REALLY AM, THEY WILL *WORSHIP* ME FOR KILLING THAT *VILE TRAITOR*, DREDD.

SUCH A PITY. SO HANDSOME, TOO, GRAMPUS. DON'T DAMAGE THIS HEAD WHEN YOU REMOVE IT.

IT WILL LEAVE HIS SHOULDERS CLEAN, JUDGE CAL.

97

99

ONLY FERGEE ALLOWED TO KILL FERGEE'S FLIES!

C-CWIPES! PW-PW-PWOTECT ME FWOM THIS BWUTE, MASTER!

CUT IT OUT, BOTH OF YOU!

WHEN THINGS HAD CALMED DOWN, DREDD OUTLINED HIS PLAN—

I NEED HELP TO GET INSIDE THE HALL OF JUSTICE UNSEEN. ALL YOU HAVE TO DO IS... *BETRAY ME!*

B-BETWAY YOU? *NEVER!*

YOU'LL DO IT, WALTER. YOU CAN START RIGHT NOW BY GETTING ON THE VID-PHONE...

SOON, AT JUSTICE CENTRAL—

WALTER THE WOBOT CALLING. THAT C-CWEEP JUDGE DWEDD HAS JUST BEEN HERE, SHOOTING GUNS AND WAISING HELL.

YOU'RE MISTAKEN, ROBOT. THERE'S NO JUDGE DWEDD ON THE FORCE.

NOT JUDGE *DWEDD*, WALTER SAY JUDGE *DWEDD*.

WE GOT US A REAL CRAZY HERE!

DREDD'S DEAD!

BUT HIS BODY WAS NEVER FOUND. WE CAN'T TAKE A CHANCE—GET SOME MEN OVER THERE QUICK.

GOOD WORK, WALTER. WE'VE GOT TO GO. JUST REMEMBER WHAT I TOLD YOU TO SAY, AND WITH LUCK CAL WILL FALL FOR IT.

WALTER WILL TWY, MASTER.

WAIT...THAT'S DREDD'S OLD ROBOT. HE'S GOT A SPEECH DEFECT...HE MUST MEAN JUDGE *DREDD!*

JUDGE DREDD

IN THE DAY THE LAW DIED!

IN ORDER TO GET A MAN INSIDE THE HALL OF JUSTICE, WHERE THE **TYRANT JUDGE CAL** RULES, **JUDGE DREDD** ENLISTS THE AID OF HIS ROBOSERVANT, **WALTER**. BUT WHEN WALTER IS TAKEN TO CAL, THINGS TURN NASTY –

IF I CAN'T KILL DREDD, AT LEAST I CAN KILL **YOU**, KNEEL, ROBOT!

YES, CHOP ME TO PIECES, GWEAT JUDGE CAL! WIP ME TO WOBO-SHWEDS! ONLY **PLEASE** DON'T SEND WALTER BACK TO THAT **CWEEP** JUDGE DREDD!

WHAT? DID YOU CALL DREDD... **A CREEP**?

B-BE BWAVE, WALTER. WEMEMBER WHAT JUDGE DWEDD TELL YOU TO SAY –

YES, A WOTTEN, UNGWATEFUL WASCAL! JUDGE DWEDD COME HOME YELLING AND SHOOTING AND MAKING A DWEADFUL MESS AND WALTER WILL NEVER SCWUB OFF ALL THAT HOWWIBLE GWEEN KLEGG BLOOD –

HURRR!

SOWWY... ALL THAT P-PWETTY GWEEN KLEGG BLOOD...

AND DO JUDGE DWEDD SAY "NICE TO SEE YOU, WALTER" OR "THANK YOU FOR KEEPING MY WOOM CLEAN, WALTER"? NO! HE SAY: "GET UP OFF YOUR KNEES, YOU SNIVELLING WOBOT!"

WALTER TWY TO BE A **GOOD** WOBOT, AND JUDGE DWEDD TWEAT HIM LIKE **WUBBISH**! BUT WALTER HAVE PWIDE! PLEASE DON'T MAKE ME GO BACK TO HIM! **I HATE HIM!**

2000AD Credit Card:
SCRIPT ROBOT J. HOWARD
ART ROBOT EWINS/McCARTHY
LETTERING ROBOT THOMAS
COMPU-73E

HMMM... PERHAPS I *WON'T* KILL THIS ROBOT. WITH HIS HELP I CAN DESTROY DREDD'S NAME *FOREVER!*

SLOCUM — SEND FOR THE *BADGEMAKER.*

AND —

I HEREBY APPOINT YOU *JUDGE WALTER* — MEGA-CITY'S FIRST ROBOT JUDGE!

A-A JUDGE! OH, WALTER IS *THRILLED!*

YOU'RE *CRAZY,* CHIEF JUDGE! THE WHOLE CITY *KNOWS* THAT ROBOT IS *SICKENINGLY LOYAL* TO DREDD.

THAT'S JUST THE *POINT,* SLOCUM! IF DREDD'S OWN ROBOT CRITICISES HIM, THE PEOPLE WILL *HAVE* TO BELIEVE IT!

BY THE WAY, SLOCUM, THE PENALTY FOR CALLING ME *CRAZY* IS DEATH. YOU *DID* CALL ME CRAZY, SLOCUM?

F-FORGIVE ME, CHIEF JUDGE — I-I DIDN'T MEAN IT! IT'S JUST THAT I... I- I WORRY FOR YOU.

DO YOU...? WHY, YES! I SEE THE WORRY LINES ALL OVER YOUR FACE. WE CAN'T HAVE THAT NOW, CAN WE?

I—I ASK ONLY TO SERVE YOU, CHIEF JUDGE.

NO, NO. WE MUST MAKE SURE YOU DON'T GET ANY MORE WORRY WRINKLES. THE QUESTION IS — HOW?

I SHALL GIVE THE MATTER SOME CONSIDERATION, SLOCUM.

BY ORDER OF JUDGE CAL, OVER THE NEXT THREE DAYS WALTER WAS GIVEN MAXIMUM EXPOSURE ON TELEVISION, TO DESTROY DREDD'S REPUTATION.

YES, FWANK, JUDGE DWEDD WAS *CWUEL.* HE USED TO BEAT WALTER WITH HIS *TWUNCHEON.*

YES, WOBIN. JUDGE DWEDD TOOK *BWIBES.* HE USED HIS BADGE TO MAKE HIMSELF WICH!

YES, WUSSEL, JUDGE DWEDD KILLED THE OLD CHIEF JUDGE! DWEDD WAS HUNGWY FOR *POWER.*

MCTV NATIONWIDE

ROBIN KNIGHT

Thursday Night PEOPLE

WITH FRIGHTENING SKILL, THE CITY'S LAST HERO WAS BEING TURNED INTO A *VILLAIN...*

EXTRA! EXTRA! MORE DIRT ON DREDD!

THAT *DREDD!* I'M BEGINNIN' TO BE GLAD HE *AIN'T* CHIEF JUDGE!

YEAH, AT LEAST YOU KNOW WHERE YOU ARE WITH CAL.

IT WAS DAYS BEFORE WALTER FOUND TIME FOR HIS REAL MISSION —

THAT'S IT FOR TONIGHT, JUDGE WALTER. TOMORROW YOU'RE BOOKED FOR *'THE LATE SHOW', 'THE LATE, LATE SHOW'* AND *THE ELK'S BANQUET.'* SO GET SOME SLEEP.

WOBOTS DO NOT NEED *SLEEP,* JUDGE WICKS. GOOD NIGHT.

WALTER *HATE* TELLING ALL THESE *LIES,* BUT IT'S THE ONLY WAY TO HELP DEAR JUDGE DWEDD

AUTHORIZED PERSONNEL ONLY

'CWIME BWIEFING WOOM'... THIS IS THE PLACE JUDGE DWEDD SAY!

117

A LARGE SPECIMEN BOTTLE STOOD BY ONE WALL, AND —

121

TO THIS END, **NERVE GAS** CONTAINERS HAVE BEEN PLACED IN EVERY DISTRICT. AT NOON TOMORROW I WILL **PERSONALLY** PRESS THE BUTTON TO **RELEASE IT!**

OH, DADDY— I'M SCARED!

IN THEIR UNDERGROUND HIDEOUT, THE JUDGES HAD INSTALLED A MONITOR –

THE BEAUTY OF THIS METHOD IS THAT IT WILL LEAVE BUILDINGS AND RECORDS INTACT, SO THAT OTHERS WHO COME HERE IN THE FUTURE MAY UNDERSTAND OUR SACRIFICE IN THE NAME OF PERFECTION!

THE MADMAN MEANS TO COMMIT MASS MURDER! THIS CHANGES OUR PLANS!

BUT PEPPER WON'T HAVE THE TAPE READY UNTIL TUESDAY!

EARLY NEXT MORNING, TWO HOURS BEFORE THE END OF CURFEW, SIX DESPERATE MEN HURRIED THROUGH THE CITY –

PAT-WAGON! DOWN!

PEPPER WILL HAVE TO FINISH IT **TONIGHT!** THERE'S NOT GOING TO **BE** ANY TUESDAY!

ALL JUDGES WERE REQUIRED TO ATTEND THE DAILY CRIME BRIEFING, WHERE CRIME REPORTS WERE FED DIRECTLY INTO THEIR BRAINS. CAL WAS USING THESE BRIEFINGS TO IMPLANT HYPNOTIC SUGGESTIONS IN THE JUDGES' MINDS, MAKING THEM LOYAL.

THE EFFECT OF DREDD'S TAPE WAS AMAZING—

MY DOK, I SEE IT NOW! CAL'S BEEN USING US LIKE... LIKE ROBOTS! HE'S TURNED US INTO CRIMINALS TO ENFORCE HIS VILE LAWS!

WE DON'T DESERVE TO BE JUDGES! WE MUST TURN OURSELVES IN AND FACE TRIAL!

NO! YOU MUST FOLLOW ME!

JUDGE DREDD!

WE NEED EVERY JUDGE ON THE FORCE TO FIGHT CAL AND HIS KLEGG MERCENARIES! YOU MUST GO ABOUT YOUR DUTIES AS NORMAL UNTIL ALL ARE PROCESSED. THE SIGNAL TO STRIKE WILL BE THE SOUND OF THE SPACE-RAID SIRENS!

SECTION AFTER SECTION WAS PROCESSED, UNTIL—

TIME IS SHORT. WE'VE GOTTA STOP CAL BEFORE HE SETS OFF THAT NERVE GAS!

IT'S NOW OR NEVER, MEN—
CHARGE!

AT THAT MOMENT CAL WAS HEADING FOR HIS APPOINTMENT WITH DEATH —

GRAMPUS

N G

THE NERVE GAS CONTAINERS HAVE BEEN PLACED IN EVERY DISTRICT. THE RELEASE CONTROL IS AT THE TOP OF THE STATUE OF JUDGEMENT!

EXCELLENT! I'LL HAVE A GRANDSTAND VIEW OF THE CITY'S FINAL MOMENTS!

PLEASE, JUDGE CAL! WE DON'T WANT TO DIE!

THAT'S ONLY NATURAL, CITIZEN. DON'T WORRY ABOUT IT!

KLEGG MERCENARIES LEAVE NOW. GOT NEW CONTRACT ON TRON PLANET — ELIMINATING SUB-SPECIES! WE GET TO *EAT* SUB-SPECIES!

SUDDENLY—

WWOOOOOO

THE CROWD FLED AT THE EERIE WAILING OF THE *SPACE-RAID* SIREN.

HE DOESN'T CARE! HE'S STARK, STARING MAD!

GOODBYE, GRAMPUS, IT'S BEEN A *PLEASURE* DEALING WITH YOU. YOU'RE SO DELIGHTFULLY VICIOUS!

HOW APPROPRIATE! THE PERFECT ACCOMPANIMENT FOR MY SUPREME ACT OF SACRIFICE.

B-BUT *WHY* ARE THE SIRENS SOUNDING?

IT JUDGE DREDD!

QUICK, CHIEF JUDGE— INTO THE HOVER-CAR!

HHRAAAIEEEEE!

RRRATTA-TAT-TAT!

I AM THE LAW NOW — AND YOU BETTER BELIEVE IT!

2000 AD Prog 89: Cover by **Mick McMahon**

2000 AD Prog 94: Cover by **Mick McMahon**

2000 AD Prog 98: Cover by **Brian Bolland**

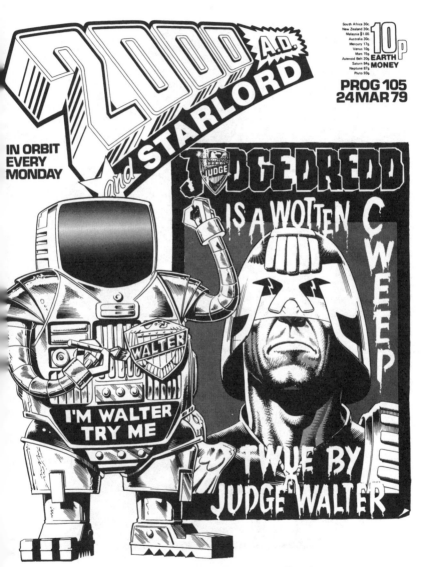

2000 AD Prog 105: Cover by **Brian Bolland**

2000 AD Prog 107: Pin-up by **Brian Bolland**

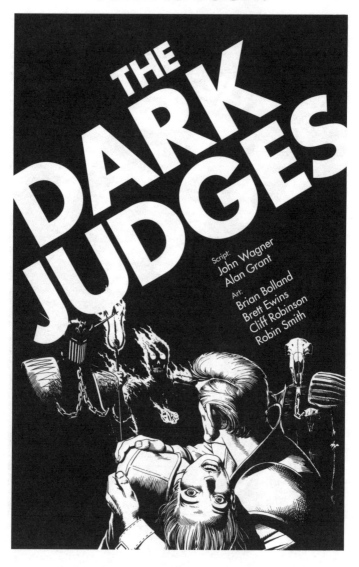